# *ideals*

## CHRISTMAS ISSUE

Light the tall and shining candles,
Hang the bunch of mistletoe,
Place the wreath of berried holly
On the door where it will show.

Deck the Christmas tree with tinsel,
Hang each silver or golden ball,
Ornament of green and yellow,
Red and blue, so none will fall.

Light the hearthfire, let the Yule log
Brightly burn to glowing embers,
Sing the joyous Christmas carols
Which each happy heart remembers.

Let the magic of this season
Stay with you and not depart;
May the Child born in a manger
Ever live within your heart.

Roy Z. Kemp

**Editorial Director,** James Kuse

**Managing Editor,** Ralph Luedtke

**Photographic Editor,** Gerald Koser

**Production Editor,** Stuart L. Zyduck

designed by

Colleen Callahan Gonring

# The Cathedral of the Pines

The towering pines raise wind-tossed heads
To meet the azure sky.
Monadnock stands majestic, strong,
Beyond the lake nearby.

It lifts high shoulders, forest-clad,
Against the glowing west,
Drawing our thoughts from things of earth
To God, for strength and rest.

The altar with its storied stones
Commands the distant view;
Its cross points worshipers to Christ,
Who transforms, makes life new.

It speaks of brotherhood and peace
Among nations great and small,
Of every race and every creed,
Says, "Welcome!" to them all.

The gold-tongued organ fills the grove
With music peaceful, sweet;
While birds with their winsome, bell-toned notes
Make worship joyful, complete.

Heaven and earth overflow with praise
By creatures large and small,
Bringing God's benediction and peace,
His blessings shower on all.

There nature's grand cathedral stands,
High on its lofty hill,
Beckoning men from earthly thoughts
To learn and live God's will.

Marion A. Manning

ISBN 0-89542-317-0  275

IDEALS—Vol. 35, No. 6—November 1978. Published bimonthly by IDEALS PUBLISHING CORPORATION, 11315 Watertown Plank Road, Milwaukee, Wis. 53226. Second-class postage paid at Milwaukee, Wisconsin. Copyright © 1978 by IDEALS PUBLISHING CORPORATION. All rights reserved. Title IDEALS registered U.S. Patent Office.

ONE YEAR SUBSCRIPTION—six consecutive issues as published—only $12.00
TWO YEAR SUBSCRIPTION—twelve consecutive issues as published—only $19.00
SINGLE ISSUES—only $2.75

*Photograph opposite*
*GRAND TETON NATIONAL PARK, WYOMING*
*Russell Lamb*

# Going Home for Christmas

Mamie Ozburn Odum

We're going home for Christmas,
We have stayed away too long;
We'll meet the loved ones waiting
With best wishes pure and strong.

We'll hang holly on the front door
And mistletoe in the hall,
Green garlands up the stairway
To welcome one and all.

We'll shout "Merry Christmas,"
As we drive o'er hills and rifts,
And every inch of space will be
Filled with gay-wrapped gifts.

But the things I'm wishing most to bring
Are wishes true and right,
And wishes for peaceful living
And inner-guiding light.

We'll sing the old hosannas
With kinfolk far and near,
We'll greet old friends and neighbors
And wish them all good cheer.

We're going home for Christmas,
A place of peace to share,
For home is where the heart is
With love beyond compare.

# Christmas Is Coming

Hustle and bustle, hurry and haste,
Never a moment that we might waste;
Shopping and wrapping, ribbons and bows,
Christmas is coming as everyone knows.

Trimmings and candles, wreath on the door,
Secrets and laughter, gladness galore,
Starlight and carols, bells ringing clear,
No other reason: Christmas is near.

Jolly Old Santa, reindeer and elves,
Presents all hidden away on the shelves,
Cards to be written, mailing to do,
Much in excitement, worries so few.

Love more abundant, peace in our heart,
Giving, remembering, smiles to impart,
Cookies and fruitcake, the fragrance of pine,
Christmas is coming to your home and mine.

Garnett Ann Schultz

# This Time of Year

Garlands of holly
   And gay mistletoe,
Friendly warm greetings,
   New-fallen snow.

Carols gaily ringing
   Good news in the air,
Everyone willing
   To help and to share.

Candlelight gleaming,
   The sparkle in eyes,
Little ones watching
   For Santa's surprise.

Loved ones returning
   From far and from near,
Isn't it the most wonderful
   Time of the year?

Kay Hoffman

# Christmas

Fluffy snow piled all around,
Bundled people shopping bound,
Christmas carols fill the air,
Rustle, bustle everywhere.
Here a greeting, there a smile,
Happy faces all the while,
Winter specter, snow and ice,
Kitchen fragrance, pungent spice,
Jingling bells, gay laughter, too,
Old traditions mixed with new;
Church bells chiming will foretell
The age-old story we know well.
Most of all, and greatest worth,
Honoring the Christ Child's birth.

Mary A. Barnard

# THE HOLLY AND THE IVY

The Holly and the Ivy,
  When they are both full grown
Of all the trees are in the wood,
  The Holly bears the crown.

O the rising of the sun,
  And the running of the deer,
The playing of the merry organ,
  Sweet singing in the choir.

The Holly bears a blossom
  As white as any flower;
And Mary bore sweet Jesus Christ
  To be our sweet Savior.

The Holly bears a berry
  As red as any blood;
And Mary bore sweet Jesus Christ
  To do poor sinners good.

The Holly bears a prickle
  As sharp as any thorn;
And Mary bore sweet Jesus Christ
  On Christmas in the morn.

The Holly bears a bark
  As bitter as any gall;
And Mary bore sweet Jesus Christ
  For to redeem us all.

The Holly and the Ivy
  Now both are full well grown:
Of all the trees are in the wood
  The Holly bears the crown.

Author Unknown

*Photograph opposite*
*Gene Ahrens*

# There Shall
# Be Music

There shall be music, sweet and clear,
Calling the reverent worshipers near,
Telling the story in notes and in rhyme
Of the Child who was born at Christmastime.

There shall be music, soft and light,
A lullaby sung on a crisp winter night,
Sweetly angelic like the voices that told
Of the birth of a king to the shepherds of old.

There shall be music, deep and strong,
Filling the air with melodious song,
Resonant sounds of gladness that tend
To lift every heart to a grateful amen!

Alice Leedy Mason

# The Songs of Christmas

The melodies of Christmastide
    that float upon the air
Are glittering gems within the
    hearts of people everywhere.

Their notes are bells of beauty,
    encircling the earth—
Proclaiming in their splendor
    the joy of Jesus' birth.

No music brings more gladness
    than those familiar airs:
A mingling of merriment
    with ardent, earnest prayers.

These tunes bring sweet nostalgia
    and flood the heart with cheer,
For the fragile songs of Christmas
    are the sweetest tunes we hear!

Cassie Eugenia Tartoué

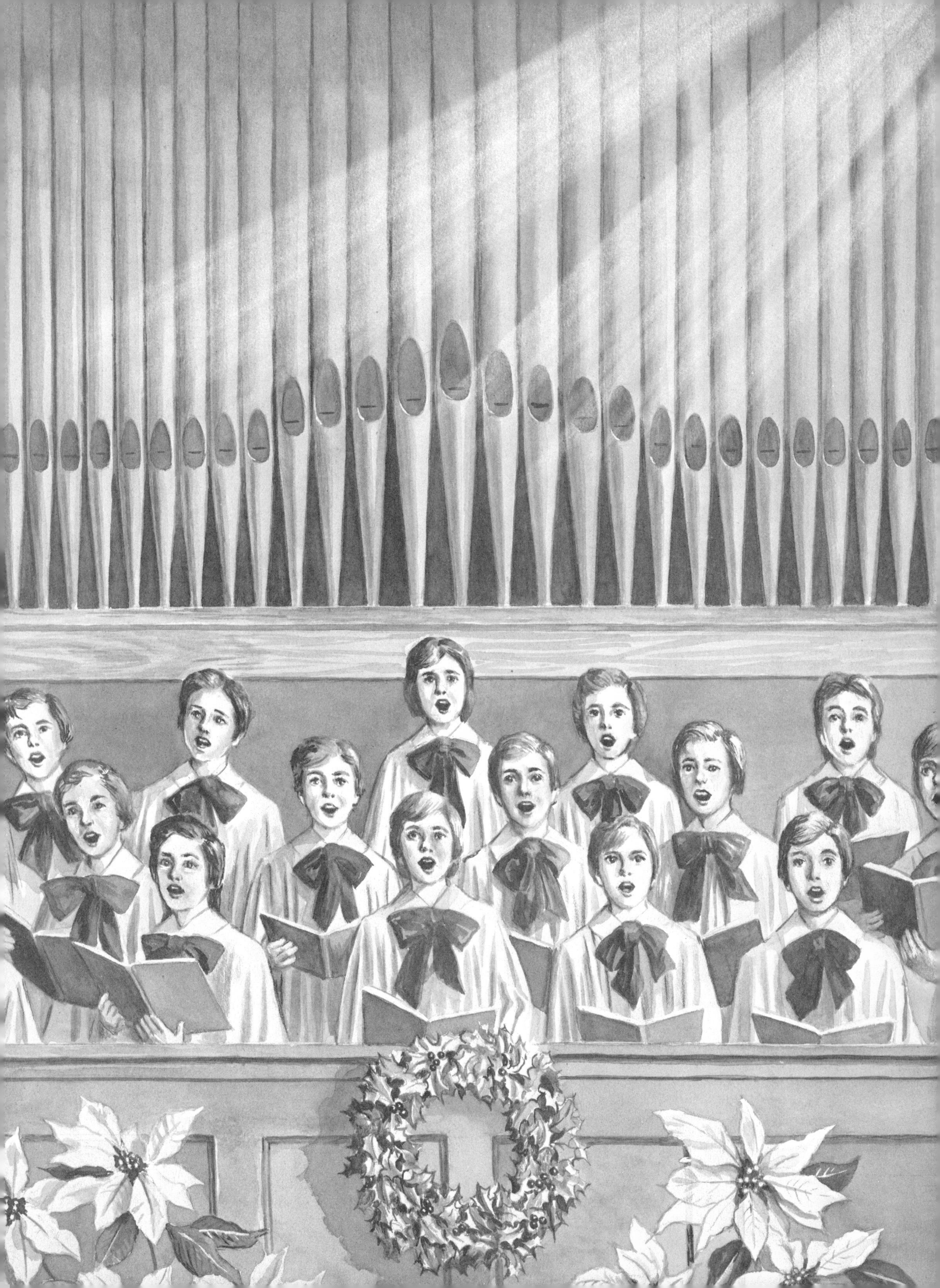

# The Meaning of Christmas

Once again it's Christmas,
Time for us to be
Busy wrapping presents
And setting up the tree,

Time to make a holly wreath
And tie it with a bow,
Time to light the candles
And hang the mistletoe,

Time to fill the stockings
With lots of little treats,
Time to stuff the turkey
And fix the candied sweets,

Time to greet our neighbors
With a handclasp and a smile,
Time to call the friends
We haven't seen for quite awhile.

It seems we have so many things
To think of and to do,
We may forget that Christmas
Has deeper meaning, too,

A meaning that goes far beyond
The things the eye can see,
Such as holly wreaths and mistletoe
And gifts beneath the tree.

For these are only symbols
Of what happened Christmas morn,
When in a lowly manger
God's only son was born.

God put him here upon this earth
With one idea in mind:
To bring new hope throughout the world
And love to all mankind.

So even though we're busy
And have many things to do,
Let's not forget that Christmas
Has this deeper meaning, too.

Let's not forget to take time out
To go to church and pray
And give the Lord his rightful due
On this, his special day.

Marge Burke

Painting opposite
John Slobodnik

# Vera Hardman

This issue marks the twenty-seventh year of our association with Vera Hardman, for it was the 1951 issue of Christmas Ideals which carried her first published poem, "Winter's Magic." This poem spoke of the beauty in a winter landscape and nature continues to be a favorite subject of Mrs. Hardman. She still seeks inspiration in the surrounding country of her native Cleveland, Ohio, often painting the scenes as well as writing of them. Throughout the years, poetic subjects have also included the Hardman cats. Some of these have been treated humorously as in "Snowflake," "The perfect gift for Mrs. Santa Claus" and "Sir Thomas Cat," "the knight of the open road." In addition to painting and writing, Mrs. Hardman enjoys reading the works of other poets and lists among her favorites those often found in the pages of Ideals.

## World of Wonder

There's a silent world of beauty
  Outside my windowpane;
For the snowflakes softly falling
  Have transformed our country lane
Into a ribbon, satin white,
  That winds away in time;
And I find myself upon this road
  Beneath the white-capped pines.

Each fence post nods quite happily
  In stocking cap of white;
And I know the joy the winter brings,
  Its magic, its delight.
In this timeless world of wonder,
  My heart so softly sings;
For angel kisses touch my cheeks
  Borne on the snowflake's wings.

## Winter's Treasure

The children, in their outstretched hands,
　Caught snowflakes large and white;
And for just a moment held there
　Jewelled stars, shining bright.

Bits of treasure from God's heaven,
　Flakes of glistening snow,
But the wonder of their beauty
　With diamond brightness glowed.

Star-shaped crystals and tiny hands,
　Soft laughter gay and warm,
For every small child's happy heart
　Knows snowflakes' magic charm.

## Christmas Card Town

Our town looks like a Christmas card,
　Glistening, happy, bright;
For feathery, starlike snowflakes
　Have fallen through the night.

The bushes all wear lacy scarves;
　The trees are cloaked in snow;
Winter's magic is everywhere
　And hearts are all aglow.

Just like a lovely Christmas card
　The message this day brings
Is "Peace on earth, goodwill to men,"
　A thought that makes hearts sing.

# To Bethlehem, with Love

### By Nathanael Olson

Bethlehem, is that really you, perched on the steep ridge of Judea's stony hill country? I thought you were a "little town" of perhaps 300 people as you were 2,000 years ago, and as I've always pictured you while singing "O Little Town of Bethlehem." But now they tell me you're filled with over 35,000 residents plus thousands of tourists who, like me, have come the four-and-a-half miles from Jerusalem to see the birthplace of our Savior.

Well, I shouldn't be surprised at your growth. A good place, like a good person, has the right to flourish. Time has a way of changing most things. Take transportation, for example. Frankly, I'd much rather be approaching you in this comfortable, air-conditioned bus than walking footsore beside a disgruntled donkey as Mary and Joseph did nineteen centuries ago.

Enough of my philosophizing! I see we're driving down your famous "Manger Street" headed for the Church of the Nativity. No doubt this is the street Phillips Brooks had in mind when he wrote:

*O little town of Bethlehem, how still we see thee lie!*
*Above thy deep and dreamless sleep the silent stars go by;*
*Yet in thy dark streets shineth the everlasting Light;*
*The hopes and fears of all the years are met in thee tonight.*

Our bus is now pulling into the parking lot across the street from The Church of the Nativity. Our Israeli guide leads the way to the place where God took human form and I, along with my daughter and forty-three American friends, push forward, anxious to see the sacred spot where Christ was born.

Minutes later, we're standing in this hallowed place—the lowly stable where Mary and Joseph found shelter when your hotel was bursting with reluctant taxpayers. A stable! What an ugly yet beautiful place for God to enter the human race. Ugly as far as worldly qualities are concerned; yet beautiful in that there was no hollow Roman pomp and circumstance to detract from the sincere love story of these two from Galilee whose humble hearts were willing to be misunderstood so God's Son could be born of a virgin as foretold by the prophet Isaiah.

The guide is now pointing to the place where Jesus was born. Then, over in a corner away from the draft, is the manger where Mary laid her baby, tightly wrapped in swaddling clothes. I glance over at Melody, my seventeen-year-old daughter. Her brown eyes are misty with tears and I feel my heart brimming with emotion. How privileged we feel to be eye-witnesses of the very birthplace of our Savior, Lord and King!

*For Christ is born of Mary; and gathered all above,*
*While mortals sleep, the angels keep their watch of wond'ring love.*
*O morning stars, together proclaim the holy birth,*
*And praises sing to God the King, and peace to men on earth.*

Loving excitement as I do, I would have enjoyed being here when the shepherds came bursting through that stable entrance, breathlessly telling the startled couple that the angels had told them this newborn child is truly the Son of God! Having said that, they knelt and worshiped the Christ. What a dramatic scene of faith, of love, of worship! While the faithless crowds snored the night away, this handful of humble men encountered God incarnate and returned to their sheep, watching with a song of eternal hope in their hearts!

*How silently, how silently the wondrous gift is giv'n!*
*So God imparts to human hearts the blessings of His Heav'n.*
*No ear may hear His coming; but in this world of sin,*
*Where meek souls will receive Him still, the dear Christ enters in.*

Perhaps if I could stay in this stable for an hour or two, I might also write a Christmas carol. But now the tour group is leaving; and so, with reluctant step, I must follow.

BETHLEHEM

Now the bus is winding up the ribbon of road between you, "the City of David" and Jerusalem, "the Holy City." I don't feel like engaging in idle chatter, but in reflecting on what I've seen. Because of you, Bethlehem, and your lowly stable where my Savior came, I understand more fully the greatest love story of all time: "For God so loved the world that He gave His only begotten Son that whosoever believeth in Him should not perish but have everlasting life" (John 3:16).

Naturally, such amazing love invites my love in return. And so I say, with Christina G. Rossetti:

*What can I give Him, poor as I am?*
*If I were a shepherd, I would bring a lamb.*
*If I were a wise man, I would do my part.*
*Yet what can I give Him? Give my heart.*

Well, I must close my love letter to you, beautiful, bustling Bethlehem. Allow me to say, "Thank you" for the tender, loving care you have shown the birthplace of my Savior, for preserving the temporal and eternal meaning of Christ's coming to earth, for being uniquely chosen by God to be the town to which Mary and Joseph had to travel ninety weary miles because of a tax decree. Surely Micah was inspired when he wrote: "But thou, Bethlehem Ephratah, though thou be little among the thousands of Judah, yet out of thee shall he come forth unto me that is to be ruler in Israel; whose goings forth have been from of old, from everlasting" (Micah 5:2).

This Christmas, I'll see you again, but in my memory. And there will be a new feeling in my voice as I join my wife and two daughters in singing:

*O holy Child of Bethlehem, descend to us, we pray;*
*Cast out our sin and enter in; be born in us today.*
*We hear the Christmas angels the great glad tidings tell;*
*O come to us, abide with us, Our Lord Emmanuel.*

# O Little Town of Bethlehem

# O Little Town of Bethlehem
## "The City of David"

Two men who dearly loved children wrote this carol for some girls and boys to sing on Christmas Day in 1868. Little did those men dream that millions of children and adults would sing this beautiful word picture about "the City of David."

The author of the words, Phillips Brooks, was an Episcopalian bishop and popular pastor of Holy Trinity Church in Boston, Massachusetts. Well-known as a gifted orator, six-foot-six bachelor, and a friend of children, he gladly came down to the level of the younger set—romping with them, laughing at their stories, sharing their smiles and tears.

On a December day in 1868, he decided to do something unusual for the children's Christmas program in his church. He would write his memories of Bethlehem where he had spent Christmas Eve three years before. Perhaps Lewis Redner, the church organist, could match these lines with a melody the children could readily learn. (As a child, Brooks had learned to sing two hundred hymns from memory.)

The Bishop began with: "O little town of Bethlehem, how still we see thee lie."

Twenty-four lines flowed from his inspired pen. He gave them to Mr. Redner, gifted musician, who not only loved music but children as well. Redner liked the words, but could not find the inspiration for an appropriate melody. Then, on the night before Christmas, he stirred from his sleep "as though awakened by an angel strain," as he later described it. Quickly, he jotted down the melody, went back to sleep, and finished harmonizing the new carol in the morning. That same day, he taught the song to the children of Holy Trinity Church. Imagine the joy they had in later years telling their children and grandchildren, "I had the thrill of singing 'O Little Town of Bethlehem' the first time it was ever heard on Christmas Day, 1868.

# Christmas Flower

Poinsettia, Christmas flower,
How you flaunt your gorgeous head,
Crowned by leafy coronet,
Brilliant ruby, Christmas red.

Carried high like torches flaming,
Lighting up the Advent time,
Heralding the Christ Child's coming
While your candles skyward climb.

Like a burning Yule log's flame,
You light up the darkest room,
Chasing out the lurking shadows,
Banishing the deepest gloom.

Poinsettia, Christmas flower,
May you live long in fact and rhyme.
Accentuating Christmas spirit
Throughout the holy Advent time.

Gladys Harp

*Photograph opposite*
*Bob Taylor*

# AN OLD-FASHIONED CHRISTMAS

The joys of an old-fashioned Christmas,
So different from those of today,
Were, nevertheless, as exciting
In their own simple, down-to-earth way.

The Christmas trees nature provided,
So carefully chosen, were fine,
Combining great beauty and stature
With the fresh scent of spruce or of pine.

The long hours we spent in preparing
The trimmings that hung on that tree
Were a part of an old-fashioned Christmas
As fun filled as any could be.

We'd whisper and giggle and titter
While toasting our shins by the fire,
Fashioning crepe-paper garlands
And popcorn balls dangling on wire.

Of home-fashioned toys there were plenty
But store-bought treasures were few;
So, oh, what a thrill Christmas morning
To get just one, shiny and new.

Our Yuletides lacked some of the glitter
That surrounds us on Christmas today;
But we'll treasure their memory forever
In our own simple, down-to-earth way.

Nadine Brothers Lybarger

# A Playful Pal

A puppy has a naughty face,
A friendly tongue and awkward grace,
Two perky ears and bark that show
What happens round him, he will know;
Big, soulful eyes that do not hide
The faithful, loving heart inside.

He tumbles into open arms,
Beguiles with eager, playful charms;
And wags his way into the heart,
Becomes a pal right from the start.
That's why boys' notes to Santa plead,
"A puppy is just what I need!"

Louise Pugh Corder

# A Purrfect Pet

A kitten has a winsome face,
Bewitching eyes, delightful grace,
Soft, fluffy fur and paws that play
With spool or yarn that roll her way,
A tongue that washes clean and neat
When she has had her mealtime treat.

She pounces onto waiting lap,
Then snuggles down for cozy nap
And purrs her way into the heart
To make one love her from the start.
That's why girls' notes to Santa say,
"Please leave a kitten Christmas Day."

Louise Pugh Corder

# The Prancing Toys

Last night when all the house was still, I woke up with a start, to lie with eyes wide open, and a quickly beating heart. Then as I listened, all at once I heard a lot of squeaks, as if the mice that run around had not been fed for weeks. I tiptoed softly down the stairs and crept towards the din, the playroom door stood open, so I carefully peeped in. The corner cupboard shook and groaned; then to my great surprise, I saw the handle start to turn before my very eyes. The cupboard door flew open and out fell all the toys. They made more noise than any of the neighbor's girls and boys.

The policeman marched along in front, his face all red and jolly, then next came by blue teddy bear, hand in hand with dolly. The fairy doll tripped lightly by, her wand a sparkling light, close on her heels my golliwog, his face as black as night. The fluffy rabbit and the dog both skipped about with glee, and everyone was chattering, a sight it was to see. The little wooden elephant gave Mickey Mouse a ride; and as he strutted on he swung his trunk from side to side. The soldiers left the castle walls and joined the merry throng, the captain led the gay parade with steps both brisk and long.

The drummer boy a gay tattoo did beat upon his drum; I never heard such merriment from toys I thought were dumb. They marched around the room and then all kinds of games they played, like hide-and-seek, and blindman's buff, oh, what a noise they made. But as the chimes of midnight struck and slowly died away, quite silent they at once became, no longer bright and gay. A solemn little band of toys, they filed across the floor, then one by one they climbed inside and closed the cupboard door. I waited for a little while, but it was all in vain; the spell had broken and they were just regular toys again.

Joan Ashurst

Lorraine Wells

# Christmas Dreaming

The small child lies asleep at last,
A favorite toy clutched in his grasp.
One could not know or e'er conceive
What dreams are his on Christmas Eve.

Perhaps he floats among the stars
And smiles at Venus, winks at Mars,
Or rides a cloud to Neverland
To walk with fairies hand-in-hand.

Perchance he sails the bounding main
Where scores of pirates gained their fame
And finds a carefully hidden lair
With secret treasure buried there.

What-e'er his dreams this Christmas Eve,
They're sure to fade, then take their leave
When Christmas Day dawns bright and clear
Mid shouts of "Santa has been here!"

*Ned Nichols*

# Christmas Morn

Close your little eyes, my child;
Drop right off to sleep,
While you dream, Old Santa's sleigh
Upon the roof will sweep.

He'll clamber down the chimney
As quietly as he can,
And though it be all sooty-black,
He'll still be spick and span.

The elves in Santa's workshop
All kinds of goodies make;
You'll find some in your stocking
In the morn when you awake.

So drift right off to dreamland;
Santa's drawing near.
The whole wide world looks brighter
On Christmas morn, my dear.

*Pauline Garms Carr*

# 'TWAS THE NIGHT BEFORE CHRISTMAS

## (The Rest of the Story)

Paul Harvey

May I present Dr. Moore.

First, so you'll feel you know him better, let me tell you about his family.

His daddy was Benjamin Moore, a Protestant Episcopal clergyman who became a bishop in that church. His daddy was also a professor at Columbia College in New York, and in 1801 he was elected president of Columbia. And Ben's nephew became president of Columbia forty or so years later.

What I'm leading up to is that our Dr. Moore had a scholarly ancestry. It was natural that he, Clement Clarke Moore, should be born with a textbook intellect. And that Clement skipped his boyhood, grew to manhood, and nobody ever called him Clem.

Dr. Moore was a scholar. Became Professor of Biblical Learning at General Theological Seminary in New York. Learned every language but slang.

In 1809 he wrote a book. It was not exactly a best seller. Its title was *A Compendious Lexicon of the Hebrew Language*.

Then Dr. Moore became full Professor of Oriental and Greek Literature. I know he hardly sounds human. But he was. Before I'm through, you'll know he was.

In 1813 the first symptom showed up. He married. At thirty-five, the professor finally looked up from his weighty reading and his pompous writing and discovered love.

Eventually, Dr. and Mrs. Moore had children of their own. With them, for the first time in his life, the professor could descend from the intellectual stratosphere and explore with them the wonderland of make-believe.

It was one day when in play, he was thus unbending ... that he authored a false statement. If he had just told it to his children, as any other father telling a fairy tale, nothing would have happened. But the meticulous professor had to put it in writing.

That did it. It was a story in verse about an old German handyman who worked for the Moores. The hired man was the model for the hero of this fiction. And a year later that flippant bit of writing almost cost the distinguished Dr. Moore a case of apoplexy.

Here's what happened.

Harriet Butler, daughter of the rector of St. Paul's Church in Troy, New York, was visiting. Somehow she saw that poem. She asked for a copy.

Dr. Moore may or may not have said she could have it. Certainly he expected her to respect the privacy of his little family joke. But she didn't.

She sent the poem anonymously to the *Troy Sentinel*. And the newspaper published it. Dr. Moore saw a copy of that paper. Even though his name was not printed, he hit the ceiling.

He could not write a protest to the newspaper without revealing that he, the dignified professor of Oriental languages, had authored this literary lie.

Besides, the *Sentinel's* story was quickly copied elsewhere. And repeatedly. What had been intended as a little private bedtime story was printed with no explanation and so was represented to be factual. Thousands came to believe it. By now there was nothing Dr. Moore could do but fume and fuss and hide and hope that nobody—particularly nobody among his associates at the seminary—ever found out his secret.

Actually, please understand, he had done nothing wrong. How many things we may say in play with our children which would appear pretty absurd in print.

Dr. Clement Moore managed to preserve his dignity with cautious silence for fifteen years. Then it got out.

In 1829 the *Troy Sentinel* discovered his identity. He threatened suit if they named him. Instead, the paper again printed his humorous little pretense and printed this explanation: "In response to many inquiries the *Sentinel* wished to state that this poem was written by a gentleman who belongs by birth and residence to the city of New York and that he is a gentleman of (more) merit as a scholar . . . ."

Well! That merely added to the authenticity of the thing and intensfied further the public curiosity as to its source. But the doctor stood firm.

He could not let this untruth be publicly associated with his distinguished name, to bring discredit upon all his truly fine writings.

In 1837, when the *New York Book of Poetry* was published, this verse was included.

It was 1838 before he ever owned up to it. Sixteen years after it was written, fifteen years after it had been published repeatedly, when Dr. Moore's children were all grown, so they could understand what had motivated their daddy to do such a thing . . . finally he told the world *The Rest of the Story*.

He told the Troy, New York, *Budget* that he did it. That he, the Episcopal man of letters who compiled the first Hebrew dictionary in the United States, that he, the distinguished Professor of Oriental and Greek Literature, that his gifted pen had been guilty of this unmitigated deception.

And so it is that this man who wrote a verse for his children is today enshrined in the hearts of all children. On the day before Christmas there will be a pilgrimage of children . . . a lantern procession to his grave in New York's Trinity Churchyard.

For you see, Dr. Clement Clarke Moore, for all the works of which he was most proud, is remembered for the one whimsical verse which embarrassed him.

Forgotten is his *Compendious Lexicon*. Remembered is the verse which he wrote for his children.

We know best his verse which begins " 'Twas the night before Christmas. . . . "

# The Hermit—A Christmas Tale

Clemens B. Glunz

Many years ago, there lived a little old hermit in the Black Forest of Germany in a cottage nestled in a stand of fir beside a remote ski trail. He wasn't much different from any other little old hermit except that he had a magnificent nativity scene in his living room; and, to magnify the exception, he didn't dismantle the scene after the Christmas season was over.

Everything in the scene—but the stable, the straw, the road, and the plaster figures—was alive, the miniature trees, the grassy terrain. There was even a miniature climbing rose that clung to the doorframe; and the scent of the pine and roses filled the air with a delicate, indescribable bouquet.

Every evening the little old hermit would sit for a while and meditate on the scene with his gruff Great Pyrenees snoring at his feet. One evening he would dwell on the uncomfortable journey Joseph and Mary spent to get to Bethlehem. Another evening he would think of the glory of the Roman emperor who had such power that he could command his subjects to return to the place of their ancestors' birth so he could count the people he ruled.

Still another evening he would contemplate the wisdom of the innkeeper who knew that his inn was not a fit place for a woman to bear a child—what with the brash revelry that goes on when people relax after a harsh journey—and told Joseph about the cozy stable-abode a Sabbath Day's distance down the road.

Most evenings, however, he would try to fathom the role Joseph played at the moment the Virgin Mary gave birth to the Infant Jesus. For, you see, no one ever took the time or thought it important to write what Joseph did to comfort his beloved spouse when the travail of bearing a child—even the Child of our Heavenly Father—was at hand.

One cold winter day in the middle of January, a famous magician, who was also a daring skier, challenged the trail that passed the little old hermit's cottage. As he was nearing the cottage, his coordination faltered for a moment and he took a nasty fall. He lay dazed for a while; when he attempted to regain his feet, he noticed that his right arm was sprained.

Panic gripped him! He was scheduled to give a performance the following week before the

emperor; and without the full use of his right arm, he was powerless to create the illusions for which he was famous.

While the magician was lying on the snow pondering his fate, a slight noise caused him to look up. There by his side stood the Great Pyrenees and coming toward him was the little old hermit. He loosed the magician's skis, helped him to his feet and invited him into his cottage, wherein he could examine his arm more closely.

Naturally, the nativity scene captured the attention of the magician the moment they entered the cottage. (After all, who has a nativity scene still in place in the middle of January?) He was about to ask the hermit why he still had the scene set up when he noticed the live plants and was conscious of the delicate bouquet that graced the air in the cottage.

The hermit gently removed the magician's shirt and examined his arm. Then he approached the nativity scene, broke a twig off one of the miniature trees and plucked a bud from the rosebush. Using the twig and the bud as a base, the little old hermit prepared a liniment. Gently he bathed the arm with the liniment and, to the utter surprise of the magician, not only did the pain leave immediately, but he regained complete use of his arm. The little hermit then insisted that the magician spend the night with him before continuing down the trail.

Early the next morning, the magician awoke to the delicious aroma of perking coffee and sizzling bacon. While the two were eating, he asked the old hermit what he could do to repay him for his

hospitality and for curing his arm. The hermit told him that whenever the magician happened to think of him, he should say a little prayer to the Infant Jesus for someone in need. The magician felt that this was certainly the least he could do and agreed with his request.

He readied himself for the trail, thanked the little old hermit again and was soon completely engrossed in navigating the treacherous descent. Little did he expect that someday the hermit would cross his path again.

That evening, while the hermit was sitting in front of the nativity scene meditating on his favorite subject, he became drowsy and the scene appeared to change before his eyes. The Infant was nowhere to be seen; only Mary and Joseph were there, sitting side by side on a colorful blanket. The Virgin seemed to whisper something in Joseph's ear and he took her right hand in both of his. Their eyes met and mirrored the depth of the purity of their love for each other.

Suddenly, two figures bright as the sun appeared momentarily and blinded the little old hermit's vision. When he regained his sight, Mary was gently placing the Infant in the manger. Then Mary and Joseph knelt in silent adoration.

The Great Pyrenees growled in his sleep and the little hermit awoke with a start. He looked at the nativity scene and a feeling of joy filled his heart. At last he knew what Joseph did at the moment Mary gave birth to the Infant Jesus. *Joseph held Mary's hand!*

The hermit could hardly contain himself with what he felt was a startling discovery.

He became so fascinated with the thought of Joseph holding Mary's hand that he decided to make a statuette of the scene and, on the following Christmas Eve, enact his own Christmas drama. He would place the statuette in the scene on Christmas Eve; and at the stroke of midnight when the bells in the village announced the arrival of Christmas Day, he would replace it with the Infant in the manger and Mary and Joseph kneeling in adoration.

One day while the hermit was in the village buying supplies, he told some of his friends about what had happened and what he intended to do on the following Christmas Eve. When they heard his story, they started to laugh at him; and soon the whole village was laughing at him.

Weeks and months flew past, and once again the Christmas season was at hand. Everyone in the village was getting ready for the festivity. And a very big day it was going to be indeed! This year, on Christmas afternoon, a famous magician was going to entertain the villagers in the town hall, and the admission was free. It was the *burgermeister's* Christmas present to the villagers.

The magician arrived two days before Christmas. He registered at the inn where he had stopped earlier that year while on a ski trip. After supper, on the way to his room, he paused outside the doorway of the *rathskeller* of the inn. At that moment, one of the villagers happened to think about the little old hermit and his quaint plans for the following day which was Christmas Eve. He thought that the story would be good for a laugh and he told it with a flourish.

The magician, standing unnoticed outside the doorway, was aghast at the way everyone made fun of the hermit. All that he could see in his mind was a nativity scene that filled a cottage with an indescribable beauty and fragrance, and a little old hermit bathing his right arm with a liniment that seemed to work a miracle.

The magician went to his room. He felt that he had to do something to stop the villagers from making fun of the hermit; but what could he do? No one in the village was aware that he knew the hermit or had heard the story as he stood outside the doorway of the *rathskeller*. This much was in his favor.

The magician thought and thought. Just when it seemed that he was helpless, a daring plan entered his mind. He would take the ski trail the next day, Christmas Eve, and stop at the hermit's cottage. Once there, he would prevail upon him to bring the statuette to the town hall before his big show on Christmas Day. As the climax to his show, he would reenact the birth of the Infant exactly as it happened in the hermit's story. He would start with the statuette of Joseph holding Mary's hand and, *presto*, the statuette would vanish before the villagers' eyes and there would be the Infant Jesus in the manger with Mary and Joseph kneeling in adoration. This would make the villagers realize that they were being unfair to the hermit. If a world-famous magician felt that Joseph held Mary's hand at the moment the Infant was born, why should they laugh at the little hermit?

The magician was so excited about his plan that he practiced the illusion far into the night. Then he lay down to sleep before he started on the trail. To his dismay, it was late in the day when he awoke. However, because the hermit had been so kind to him, he was still determined to carry out his plan.

The magician donned his ski apparel and started out. Darkness overcame him, but by the light of a bright moon, he managed to reach the old hermit's cottage shortly before midnight. As he was about to knock on the door, he heard the Great Pyrenees whimpering softly inside the cottage. The magician found the little old hermit slumped forward in his chair before the nativity scene in which, just as he had heard in the story, was the statuette of Joseph holding Mary's hand.

Sadness tore at the heart of the magician when he realized that the hermit would not be able to complete his Christmas drama. Tenderly, he lifted him in his arms and lay him on a cot opposite the scene. At that moment, the bells in the village announced the arrival of Christmas Day and the magician was aware of a strange light momentarily illuminating the cottage.

Startled, he turned, and his gaze fell immediately on the nativity scene.

The statuette had vanished and, in its place, Mary and Joseph knelt in silent adoration of the Infant in a manger.

*Overleaf painting*
FARM IN WINTER
C. I. Dreisbach

C.L.DREISBACH

# Vision

Last night I crept across the snow,
Where only tracking rabbits go,
And then I waited quite alone
Until the Christmas radiance shone!

At midnight, twenty angels came,
Each white and shining like a flame.
At midnight, twenty angels sang,
The stars swung out like bells and rang.

They lifted me across the hill,
They bore me in their arms until
A greater glory greeted them.
It was the town of Bethlehem.

And gently, then, they set me down,
All worshiping that holy town,
And gently, then, they bade me raise
My head to worship and to praise.

And gently, then, the Christ smiled down.
Ah, there was glory in that town!
It was as if the world were free
And glistening with purity.

And in that vault of crystal blue,
It was as if the world were new,
And myriad angels, file on file,
Gloried in the Christ Child's smile.

It was so beautiful to see
Such glory, for a child like me,
So beautiful, it does not seem
It could have been a Christmas dream.

John Farrar

# The Christmas Story

And it came to pass in those days, that there went out a decree from Caesar Augustus, that all the world should be taxed. And all went to be taxed, every one into his own city. And Joseph also went up from Galilee, out of the city of Nazareth, into Judaea, unto the city of David, which is called Bethlehem; to be taxed with Mary his espoused wife, being great with child. And so it was, that, while they were there, the days were accomplished that she should be delivered. And she brought forth her firstborn son, and wrapped him in swaddling clothes, and laid him in a manger; because there was no room for them in the inn (Luke 2:1-7).

And there were in the same country shepherds abiding in the field, keeping watch over their flock by night. And, lo, the angel of the Lord came upon them, and the glory of the Lord shone round about them: and they were sore afraid. And the angel said unto them, Fear not: for, behold, I bring you good tidings of great joy, which shall be to all people. For unto you is born this day in the city of David a Savior, which is Christ the Lord. And this shall be a sign unto you; Ye shall find the babe wrapped in swaddling clothes, lying in a manger. And suddenly there was with the angel a multitude of the heavenly host praising God, and saying, Glory to God in the highest, and on earth peace, goodwill toward men (Luke 2:8-14).

And it came to pass, as the angels were gone away from them into heaven, the shepherds said one to another, Let us now go even unto Bethlehem, and see this thing which is come to pass, which the Lord hath made known unto us. And they came with haste, and found Mary, and Joseph, and the babe lying in a manger. And when they had seen it, they made known abroad the saying which was told them concerning this child. And all they that heard it wondered at those things which were told them by the shepherds. But Mary kept all these things, and pondered them in her heart. And the shepherds returned, glorifying and praising God for all the things that they had heard and seen, as it was told unto them (Luke 2:15-20).

Now when Jesus was born in Bethlehem of Judaea in the days of Herod the king, behold, there came wise men from the east to Jerusalem, saying, Where is he that is born King of the Jews? for we have seen his star in the east, and are come to worship him. When Herod the king had heard these things, he was troubled, and all Jerusalem with him. And when he had gathered all the chief priests and scribes of the people together, he demanded of them where Christ should be born. And they said unto him, In Bethlehem of Judaea: for thus it is written by the prophet, And thou Bethlehem, in the land of Juda, art not the least among the princes of Juda: for out of thee shall come a Governor, that shall rule my people Israel. Then Herod, when he had privily called the wise men, inquired of them diligently what time the star appeared. And he sent them to Bethlehem, and said, Go and search diligently for the young child; and when ye have found him, bring me word again, that I may come and worship him also. When they had heard the king, they departed; and, lo, the star, which they saw in the east, went before him, till it came and stood over where the young child was. When they saw the star, they rejoiced with exceeding great joy. And when they were come into the house, they saw the young child with Mary his mother, and fell down, and worshiped him: and when they had opened their treasures, they presented unto him gifts; gold, and frankincense, and myrrh (Matt. 2:1-11).

# Keeping Christmas

It is a good thing to observe Christmas day.
The mere marking of times and seasons, when men agree to stop work
and make merry together, is a wise and wholesome custom.
It helps one to feel the supremacy of the common life over the individual life.
It reminds a man to set his own little watch, now and then,
by the great clock of humanity which runs on sun time.

But there is a better thing than the observance of Christmas day,
and that is keeping Christmas.

Are you willing to forget what you have done for other people,
and to remember what other people have done for you;
to ignore what the world owes you, and to think what you owe the world;
to put your rights in the background, and your duties in the middle distance,
and your chances to do a little more than your duty in the foreground;
to see that your fellowmen are just as real as you are,
and try to look behind their faces to their hearts hungry for joy;
to own that probably the only good reason for your existence
is not what you are going to get out of life, but what you are going to give to life;
to close your book of complaints against the management of the universe,
and look around you for a place where you can sow a few seeds of happiness—
are you willing to do these things even for a day?
Then you can keep Christmas.

Are you willing to stoop down and consider the needs and the desires of little children;
to remember the weakness and loneliness of people who are growing old;
to stop asking how much your friends love you,
and ask yourself whether you love them enough;
to bear in mind the things that other people have to bear in their hearts;
to try to understand what those who live in the same house with you really want,
without waiting for them to tell you;
to trim your lamp so that it will give more light and less smoke,
and to carry it in front so that your shadow will fall behind you;
to make a grave for your ugly thoughts and a garden for your kindly feelings,
with the gate open—
are you willing to do these things even for a day?
Then you can keep Christmas.

Are you willing to believe that love is the strongest thing in the world—
stronger than hate, stronger than evil, stronger than death—
and that the blessed life which began in Bethlehem nineteen hundred years ago
is the image and brightness of the Eternal Love?
Then you can keep Christmas,

And if you can keep it for a day, why not always?
But you can never keep it alone.

Henry van Dyke

# Christmas Eve Services

On Christmas Eve in our church,
  There's bustle in the air
And super-charged expectancy
  As "little" choirs prepare.

When you worship with the children,
  You feel so close to Him—
You can see in those excited eyes
  A star that never will dim.

Though the sanctuary rustles,
  The story stays the same,
And each worshiper within it
  Knows joy to praise His name!

Families of young folk exit,
  Others come to find a place;
And the smiles that pass between them
  Show love on every face.

Holy Christmas comes to our church
  In a myriad of ways,
And we thank God for sending us
  The happiest of days!

Marilyn Findlay

# Happy Birthday, Jesus

All the way to Bethlehem
   As Jóab walked along,
His father told of the promise old,
   And of the angel's song.

What could a shepherd boy, he thought,
   Give to a newborn king?
For the men brought lambs and herbs or jam,
   But he had none to bring.

"Be still, small Jóab, don't you fret.
   The city's not too far.
Lambs must be led," his father said,
   "But you can see the star!

"Soon we will rest beside the well
   Where travelers feed their flocks.
Don't stray off course—you'll lose your horse
   To bandits in the rocks."

A coin would buy a tiny chest
   With leather latch and strings.
A coin, he thought, might well have bought
   Some very special things.

Maybe a horse like grandpa made
   To fill his heart with joy.
But coins were things for sons of kings.
   Not for a shepherd boy!

The way grew long for small Jóab
   So his father made a pack.
The boy, of course, and his little horse
   Would ride upon his back.

At last they arrived at Bethlehem,
   These shepherds from afar,
Where they were led to the manger bed
   By the light of the eastern star.

Small Jóab saw his father's gift—
   A lamb—all he could bring.
Then the shepherd boy gave his favorite toy
   For the birthday of the King!

Alice Leedy Mason

# A Dickens of a Dinner

Peggy Daum

"Food, glorious food," as Oliver Twist sings in a modern musical, is important to nearly every character Charles Dickens ever created.

Whether it be a poor boy like Oliver or a man of comfortable means like old Fessiwig, Dickens' characters loved the feasting and the merriment of a great party. His characters were a reflection of the author himself and the people he knew. And no one loved a party more than Dickens.

The Christmases of many years, relived by Ebenezer Scrooge in *A Christmas Carol*, are very nearly the Christmases of Dickens' own boyhood and manhood. With ten growing children and a wide circle of friends, Dickens presided over many a splendid holiday gathering, many a festive dinner.

What kind of a meal did Dickens like? "Asparagus soup and white soup" to start. Then "boiled salmon, lobster sauce, filleted soles and shrimp sauce" for entrees. Then the main course—"patties, pork cutlets, lobster ditto, grenadine of veal, rabbit curry, forequarter of lamb, chickens and tongue, spinach, potatoes, salad, guinea fowl, pigeons, lobster salad and asparagus." And finally the desserts—"cabinet pudding, punch jelly, charlotte russe, clear jelly and Italian cream."

Of course, that was for fourteen to twenty persons. If only eight to ten were expected, a winter meal might consist of only twenty-five items instead of twenty-six. "Vermicelli soup and oxtail soup; turbot, smelts, stewed eels, soles and cod's heads; fricassee chicken, oyster patties, stewed kidneys, roast sweetbreads, two boiled fowls, ham, pigeon pie, saddle of mutton, three woodcocks, hare, two wild ducks, mashed potatoes and broccoli; apple tart, orange fritters, charlotte russe and Italian cream; macaroni and toasted cheese."

Eating in the Dickensian style is well recorded in a cookbook, *What Shall We Have for Dinner?* written by a Lady Maria Clutterbuck and printed in 1851 and 1852 by Dickens' publisher, Bradbury and Evans.

Lady Maria Clutterbuck was the pseudonym of Catherine Hogarth Dickens, the author's wife. Putting on a play was often part of an evening's entertainment, and Mrs. Dickens once portrayed a character by that name. The book was published shortly before their tenth child was born.

The menus Mrs. Dickens recommends in her slim, fifty-five page volume could have been written for the sumptuous feasts her husband describes in his writings.

In her preface, she introduces her husband, "the late Sir Jonas Clutterbuck," as a man who had, "in addition to a host of other virtues, a very good appetite and an excellent digestion."

She attributes their happy life and his "general practice" of dining at home, rather than staying at the club, to the fact that she always provided meals of which he approved. She says that she consented to share her menus "to rescue fair friends from (the) domestic suffering of wondering what to serve for dinner."

And she proceeds to supply more than 170 menus for from two to twenty persons, plus a few recipes, all of which, it is said, "amused" her husband and were generally well received by his critics—with the exception of one reviewer who observed that "no man could possibly survive the consumption of such frequent toasted cheese!"

Cooks are on their own to produce most of the items listed in the menus, but "useful receipts" are provided for twenty-seven dishes.

They range from brief directions for hominy ("boil Indian corn in milk, add sugar or salt according to taste") and rice blancmange ("boil rice in milk, put into a mold, and let stand until cold") to more lengthy descriptions, such as salmon curry, but none seem overly complicated.

*Photograph opposite*
*Gerald Koser*

# Mrs. Dickens' Useful Recipes

## Salmon Curry

"Have two slices of salmon weighing about a pound each, which cut into pieces of the size of walnuts, cut up two middling-size onions, which put into a stew-pan with an ounce of butter and a clove of garlic cut in thin slices, stir over the fire till becoming rather yellowish, then add a teaspoon of curry powder, and half that quantity of curry paste; mix all well together with a pint of good broth, beat up and pass through a tammy into a stew-pan, put in salmon, which stew about half-an-hour, pour off as much of the oil as possible; if too dry, moisten with a little more broth, mixing it gently, and serve as usual with rice separate. Salmon curry may also be made with the remains left from a previous dinner, in which case reduce the curry sauce until rather thick before putting in the salmon, which only requires to be made hot in it. The remains of a turbot may also be curried in the same way, and also any kind of fish."

The next two recipes would fit comfortably into a budget-minded menu of today. It is said that Mrs. Dickens dined at the fashionable restaurant of Chef M. Alexis Soyer in 1851 and was encouraged by his example to publish her book.

## Steak a la Soyer

"The rump steak to be broiled, and to be dressed with pepper, salt, cayenne and flour, all in a dredge box together, keep constantly turning the steak and dredging it; chop up one small shallot, put it in a stew-pan with a little ketchup, when the steak is sufficiently done add a little butter to it, strain the sauce through a small sieve, and serve very hot."

## Kalecannon

"Boil three or four carrots tender, some nice young greens, a few turnips, a few potatoes; cut off the outsides of the carrots and chop them up very fine, also chop the greens, mash the turnips and potatoes, then place it in a melon shape to form the stripes of colour, filling up the interior of the mould with all the vegetables chopped up together with pepper and salt. Butter the mould and boil half-an-hour."

Occasionally, there is additional useful information, such as the last sentence of this soup recipe.

## Mutton Broth

"The best part of the mutton from which to make good broth is the chump end of the loin, but it may be made excellently from the scrag end of the neck only, which should be stewed gently for a long time (full three hours, or longer if it be large) until it becomes tender, but not boiled to rags as it usually is; a few grains of whole pepper, with a couple of fried onions and some turnips, should be put along with the meat an hour or two before sending up the broth, which should be strained from the vegetables, and chopped parsley and thyme be mixed in it; the turnips should be mashed and served in a separate dish to be eaten with the mutton with parsley-and-butter or caper sauce. If meant for persons in health, it ought to be strong or it will be insipid; the cooks usually skim it frequently, but if given as a remedy for a severe cold, it is much better not to remove the fat, as it is very healing to the chest."

This is the recipe for Italian cream mentioned frequently in the menus.

## Italian Cream

"Whip together for nearly an hour a quart of very thick scalded cream, a quart of raw cream, the grated rind of four lemons and the strained juice, with 10 ounces of white powdered sugar, then add half-a-pint of sweet wine, and continue to whisk it until it becomes quite solid; lay a piece of muslin in a sieve, and ladle the cream in upon it with a spoon; in twenty hours turn it carefully out, but mind it does not break, garnish it with fruit, jelly, or with flowers."

*It is good to be children sometimes,*
*And never better than at Christmastime.*

*Charles Dickens*

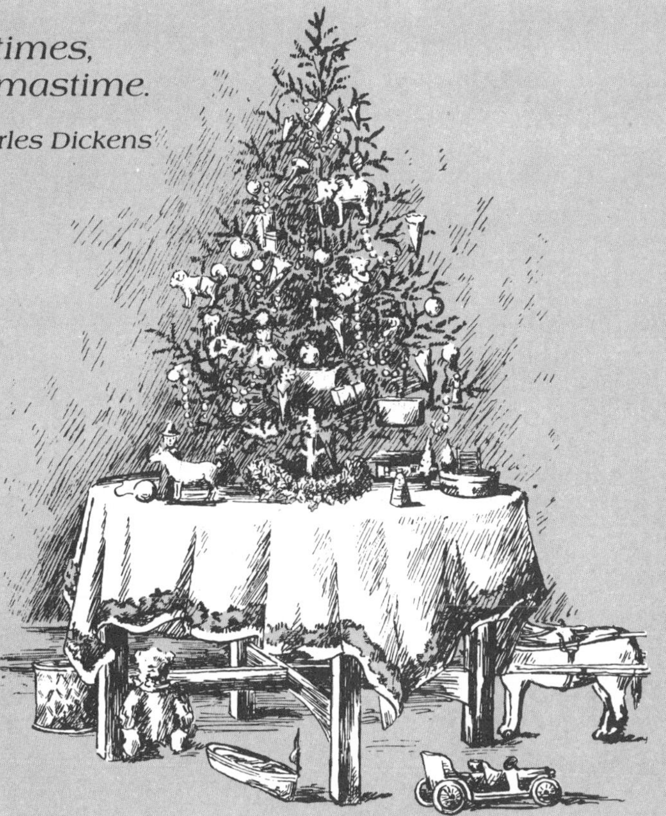

# *Homecoming Hearts*

At Christmastime when hearts are warm,
As sheltered from the winter storm,
We gather at our Christmas tree;
God's love is there, as meant to be.

Though filled with gifts, good food and fun,
Deep in the soul of every one
Abides the Babe of Bethlehem,
Down to the youngest one of them.

Though years bring change and paths will stray,
There shines that star each Christmas Day;
Earth knows no paths mankind may roam
Too far from memories of home.

D. A. Hoover

*Photograph opposite*
*Three Lions, Inc.*

# THE LADIES' HOME JOURNAL

## CHRISTMAS 1890

# MOTHERS' CORNER

### EDITED BY ELISABETH ROBINSON SCOVIL

*We are featuring the following article as it appeared in the Ladies' Home Journal, 1890. You can see the message has remained constant over the last century. We hope you enjoy this approach to the universal joy expressed at Christmastime.*

The very name of December as it comes in sight on our calendars, or gazes at us from the newly turned pages of our almanacs, gives us a thrill of pleasure with its warm suggestion of Christmas greetings and festivities. Each Christmas brings its special delights, more sober and chastened as we learn to find our own joy in the happiness of others, instead of expecting others to provide it for us.

Christmas is indeed the children's feast; hallowed by the remembrance of the Holy Child born, as on this day, at Bethlehem. To every mother the thought of the Virgin mother rejoicing over her firstborn, with no foreboding as yet of the sword that was to pierce her own soul, must come with a peculiar nearness that calls forth an answering glow of sympathy and tenderness.

The sword comes to each in turn. Even if the bitter trials of loss and bereavement are spared, the children go, the years steal them away. Let them be made happy while they stay. The tenderest love and the fullest indulgence can do them no harm if generosity and unselfishness are the lessons of their daily life, taught by precept and by example.

Gifts are the great consideration at Christmas. Thought of and dreamed of for weeks before by the children. Pondered over and worried over for more than the same length of time, by the busy mother of small means. Each of the darlings must have something, and how to bring the presents within the limit of the narrow income, which it is so hard to stretch to cover the daily wants, is a puzzle that would bewilder the wisest head.

When there is not much money to spare do not fritter it away on a number of little things, but spend each one's share in some substantial gift that can be kept as a remembrance. It need not be intrinsically valuable, but let it be something that the child can keep, with reasonable care, as a memento of the happy Christmas at home. A certain china box with figures of a boy and girl feeding chickens on the cover, that once delighted the heart of a little girl of five, is still, after nearly forty years, one of her chief treasures. The sight of the quaint coloring brings remembrances that are almost overpowering in their strength and sweetness. It is a fragment of the past, and precious as the last glimpse of the long-vanished fairyland of sheltered childhood.

Mothers are making now the memories that are to be the inheritance of their children during all their lives. Let there be a few words of tenderness and blessing to recall when they look back with full hearts on those happy Christmas mornings. Let the sound of one of the grand old hymns that have expressed the Christmas joy of so many generations mingle with them. Its music will then always bring the echo of the voice that made the very centre and core of home.

The touch of solemnity will not dampen the children's mirth, only soften and sweeten it, making the day, in the truest sense of the dear words of greeting—A MERRY CHRISTMAS.

Elisabeth Robinson Scovil

# Home for Christmas

Going home again for Christmas
  Will always bring to mind,
The home folks who are waiting there
  With smiles so sweet and kind.

I am going home for Christmas
  Is a song my heart sings;
I can scarcely wait the morrow
  For the joy that it brings.

A small house in the country
  Where smoke curls in the air,
The log fire where the flames leap high,
  A cozy rocking chair.

The shadows of the eventide
  Are falling across the snow,
And bathe the earth in purple mist
  While winter's sun's bright glow.

A friendly church is beckoning
  With spire so slim and tall,
Bells that chime a happy welcome
  To all who heed its call.

Reflects itself within my heart.
  I'm happy as can be,
For I'm going home for Christmas
  To all these memories.

*Vera Hardman*

*Merry Christmas, Friend*

When the Christmas chimes are ringing
And gay Yuletide songs we're singing
And so many expectations fill the air,
Like the past ones we remember,
It's another bright December;
Come and join the fun. It's Christmas everywhere!

There are wreaths of pine and holly
And a Santa Claus who's jolly
(Seems we see him almost everywhere we go)
With a plumped-up lap to sit on
That all children seem to fit on,
And they love to hear his hearty, "Ho, ho, ho!"

There are cheerful words of greeting
That the grown-ups keep repeating,
"Merry Christmas!" and "A Happy Holiday!"
And our hearts are filled with rapture
As the season's mood we capture,
Each to pass it on in his own special way.

There's a lot of love and caring
That I'm sure you will be sharing
And it goes with every message that I send.
May you have some special reason
To be gay this Yuletide season.
"May you have a very merry Christmas, friend!"

*Nadine Brothers Lybarger*

*My*
*Favorite Gift*

My favorite gift for Christmas
isn't boxed and wrapped and tied.
It's the warm and friendly feeling
that keeps glowing deep inside.

It's the warm and loving feeling
that keeps bidding me to share
whatever bounty I possess
until my cupboard's bare.

It's the warm and kindly feeling
that turns stranger into friend
and prompts a cheery word and smile
as down the street I wend.

It's the good old Christmas spirit
that would be most greatly missed,
so I put it first and foremost
on my Christmas wishing list.

Virginia Blanck Moore

# Christmas Comes in Softly

Christmas comes in softly,
Soon you see it there,
In fancy foods and children's eyes,
Holly wreaths and angel hair.

It whispers past your window
On a cold and snowy night;
You see it on the frosty panes
In every candle burning bright.

See the bright star shining
Far off in the east;
Hear the ancient carols ringing
Joyous Noels claiming peace.

Christmas comes in softly
As a feeling in the air;
Keep your heart alive and listen;
See and hear it everywhere!

D. R. Barnes

# The Real Christmas

Pat Boone

It takes two to make Christmas. Christ—and you. Christ—and me. That, I think, is the truth about the *real* Christmas

You know, we're born with the spirit of *getting* (at least I was!) and we develop the spirit of *giving* only after we recognize the childish "gimmes" and are willing to release them (at least I did!). . . .

Robert Young and I play golf once in a while. I remember a wonderful story he told about his youngest daughter and the night she began to grow up for sure—to "put away childish things." Until then, according to Bob, the evening prayers she said while they knelt beside her bed sounded more like a kid's letter to Santa Claus than anything else. "She'd reel off a list of things she wanted done and while they changed from time to time, the list didn't seem to get shorter. Then one night when she had plowed confidently through her requests there was quite a pause without the final 'amen.' I just knelt there and waited and finally she said, in a very small voice, as if she had heard what she was saying for the first time: 'And now, dear Lord, is there anything I can do for you?' "

And that seems to me to be the place where I always have to start my Christmas giving. After all, I remind myself, whose birthday is it, anyway? I knew a little boy whose mother told him Christmas was Jesus' birthday and immediately he demanded: "How many candles does *He* have on *His* cake?" Now I somehow don't think with all those stars of His He needs any candles on a cake—but there *are* things we can do for Him, things He asked us to do in connection with *giving*. He mentioned a *step of preparation for giving* which should come first: "Therefore if thou bring thy gift to the altar, and there rememberest that thy brother hath ought against thee; Leave there thy gift before the altar, and go thy way; first be reconciled to thy brother, and then come and offer thy gift" (Matthew 5:23-24).

Now, that's plain enough even for me to understand—and what a wonderful spirit in which to approach Christmas! Wouldn't that be a great gift for the One whose message

was "Love one another"? If, before Christmas Day, each one of us who professes to follow Him actually went around and called on each individual who is cross with us or whom we have hurt, each one with whom we have a peeve or who has hurt us, so that we didn't have a bad friend, or a hurt feeling, or a hate, or resentment, in our whole beings? Imagine if everyone who celebrated Christmas did this! I've got a feeling it would be a hundred times as sensational and a thousand times more useful to mankind than landing something or someone on Mars. . . .

Because love is the spirit of Christmas. Love was in the heart of God when He gave us the Gift. Love was in the heart of Christ when He lived and died for us. The Christmas spirit, love, changes hearts and lives.

*When?* It can happen to us now. This minute. This Christmas. In our own Hometown, U.S.A., in our own twentieth century, if we'll let Christ enter our individual minds and hearts. The minute that we do, the Child is born unto *us.* Then His government can take over our individual lives, not only on His birthday but every day. Always.

# Christmas and New Year Bells

The time draws near the birth of Christ:
    The moon is hid; the night is still;
The Christmas bells from hill to hill
    Answer each other in the mist.

Four voices of four hamlets round,
    From far and near, on mead and moor,
Swell out and fail, as if a door
    Were shut between me and the sound:

Each voice four changes on the wind,
    That now dilate, and now decrease,
Peace and goodwill, goodwill and peace,
    Peace and goodwill, to all mankind.

This year I slept and woke with pain,
    I almost wish'd no more to wake,
And that my hold on life would break
    Before I heard those bells again:

But they the troubled spirit rule,
    For they controll'd me when a boy;
They bring me sorrow touch'd with joy,
    The merry, merry bells of Yule.

Ring out, wild bells, to the wild sky,
    The flying cloud, the frosty light:
The year is dying in the night;
    Ring out, wild bells, and let him die.

Ring out the old, ring in the new,
    Ring, happy bells, across the snow:
The year is going, let him go;
    Ring out the false, ring in the true.

Ring out the grief that saps the mind,
    For those that here we see no more;
Ring out the feud of rich and poor,
    Ring in redress to all mankind.

Ring out a slowly dying cause,
    And ancient forms of party strife;
Ring in the nobler modes of life,
    With sweeter manners, purer laws.

Ring out the want, the care, the sin,
    The faithless coldness of the times;
Ring out, ring out my mournful rhymes,
    But ring the fuller minstrel in.

Ring out false pride in place and blood,
    The civic slander and the spite;
Ring in the love of truth and right,
    Ring in the common love of good.

Ring out old shapes of foul disease,
    Ring out the narrowing lust of gold;
Ring out the thousand wars of old,
    Ring in the thousand years of peace.

Ring in the valiant man and free,
    The larger heart, the kindlier hand;
Ring out the darkness of the land,
    Ring in the Christ that is to be.

*Alfred, Lord Tennyson*

*Photograph opposite*
*Bob Taylor*

# The Lasting Part of Christmas

Do keep the joys of Christmas
Though Christmas Day is past,
This is the one bright shining part
That evermore can last,
The special sounds forgotten,
The music tucked away,
The tree is just a memory
The Yule log bright and gay.

Yet keep the joys of Christmas,
Though toys are tossed aside,
And ornaments no longer there.
The tree has long since died,
The candles melt to nothingness,
The wrappings are no more,
The postman bringing packages
No longer at the door.

Do keep the love of Christmas,
For this alone can be
More precious than the greetings bright,
More lasting than the tree.
The tinsel, bows and mistletoe
Are only for a day,
But love and joys forever live
In hearts that kneel and pray.

The lasting part of Christmas,
The treasures that we keep,
Though magic moments fade away
And dreams are gone with sleep,
The quiet glowing wonder
That Christmas doth impart,
'Tis this and this alone can live
Each day within your heart.

Garnett Ann Schultz

Christmas ISSUE

*ideals*

Ideals' Pages from the Past

On the following six pages, we are presenting a selection from Christmas Ideals 1953.

A law was written in the stars
  Two thousand years ago;
It mellowed aged shepherd hearts
  And cast a golden glow—
Reflected from celestial heights
  To one rude stall below.

*The law of love's eternal fire*
  *Was penned that starry night,*
*The Fatherhood of God to man—*
  *An awesome, holy sight,*
*Across a darkened world of sin—*
  *A bursting beam of light.*

It said to all the ages past
  And centuries to be
That deep within each human breast
  There dwelt eternity—
A spark not kindred to our dust—
  Unquenchable and free.

           *Alice E. Kennelly*

# Santa's Record Book

Ben Sweeney

My dear old Mother told me
   Many, many years ago,
That Santa kept a record book
   So he'd be sure to know—
When Christmas time came 'round again—
   My bad deeds for the year,
And all the misbehavior
   Of children far and near;

I shudder now to think of what
   Those pages might reveal,
And if he read the book, how would
   My own son Jimmie feel?
For there in letters cold and black,
   Accusing through the years,
Would be my own long list of pranks—
   My diary of tears!

And Jim would look at me askance
   And never ever more
Pay heed to careful lectures on
   My *better* days of yore;
So Santa, keep your Record Book
   Well under lock and key;
Inscribe the deeds you must, of course,
   But *never let us see!*

©

# A Wish At Christmas

George Z. Keller

I am sitting by the Christmas tree,
We have trimmed it once again,
It stands a glowing symbol
In the humble hearts of men,
It captivates the children
And holds them in great awe,
Their wondering eyes behold the sight
Which first the Christ Child saw.

They view the glistening tinsel,
And the brightly colored balls;
The vari-colored, shimmering lights
Cast shadows on the walls.
The sturdy balsam branches,
Brought lately from the woods,
Will soon be drooping with the weight
Of Santa's precious goods.

And, underneath, is scattered 'round,
A great array of things:
Queer animals of every sort—
A bird that never sings;
A tiny church, a mirrored pond
Where swim a duck or two;
A lighted house with chimney bright,
And Santa dropping through.

I stand and view the picture
With reverence in my heart,
For the eyes of men and children
Are a separate thing apart;
But, somehow, I keep wishing
Father Time could be beguiled
To let me see a tree once more
Through the wondering eyes of a child.

©

# Song of Joy

*Elsie E. Thornburg*

Sing for joy, O people sing;
Good tidings to you today we bring,
   For unto you down Bethlehem way
A Child is born — is born today.

*Sing ye people, O people sing!*
*Sing for joy; let your voices ring,*
   *For in Bethlehem in early morn,*
*In David's city, a Saviour is born.*

   An Angel came to earth today
To bring the message all the way;
   The baby born is Christ the King,
Who to the world will gladness bring.

*O come ye people and worship him!*
*Let loud hosannas to Him ring*
   *Until this message covers the earth*
*And hearts of men shall know rebirth.*

# The Old Amaze

These are the things I pray the years may leave
Untarnished and untouched by dust and blight:
The old amaze, the spell of Christmas Eve,
Its rapture and delight,

The breathless wonder that the stars awake,
The unfaltering belief that a star once led
Three kings a devious way—that it still can take
Men to Christ's manger bed.

And hurrying years, in passing let us keep
Some starry-eyed expectancy aglow:
The thing that children, waking from their sleep
On Christmas morning, know.

And, oh, some little flame of eagerness!
Years, leave it lighted as you pass, I pray:
A little inner flame to lift and bless
All hearts on Christmas Day.

Grace Noll Crowell

"The Old Amaze" from THE GOLDEN SUMMIT by Grace Noll Crowell. Copyright
1937 by Harper & Row, Publishers, Inc.; renewed 1965 by Grace Noll Crowell.
Reprinted by permission of the publisher.

Coming in Friendship Ideals—

A special feature story on nodding figurines, appropriately called "Nodders" . . . the popular tale "Stone Soup" . . . Ideals Best-Loved Poet James J. Metcalfe . . . Pages from the Past, Friendly Ideals, 1947 . . . plus a collection of poetry and prose expressing the warmth and beauty of friendship.

ACKNOWLEDGMENTS

Excerpts from THE REAL CHRISTMAS by Pat Boone. Copyright © 1961 by Fleming H. Revell Company. Used by permission. A DICKENS OF A DINNER by Peggy Daum. From THE MILWAUKEE JOURNAL, December 16, 1970. Used with permission. PRAYER by John Farrar. From SONGS FOR PARENTS by John Farrar. Copyright © 1921 by Yale University Press. THE HERMIT—A CHRISTMAS TALE by Clemens B. Glunz. © 1973, All Rights Reserved, Clemens B. Glunz. Cover of THE LADIES' HOME JOURNAL, Christmas 1890 and MOTHER'S CORNER, edited by Elisabeth Robinson Scovil, © 1890 Curtis Publishing Co. Reprinted by permission of LADIES' HOME JOURNAL. KEEPING CHRISTMAS by Henry van Dyke from SPIRIT OF CHRISTMAS is reprinted by permission of Charles Scribner's Sons. Copyright 1905 Charles Scribner's Sons.

Additional photo credits: Front cover, Robert Cushman Hayes. Inside front cover, Ouray, Colorado, Alpha Photo Associates. Inside back cover, Grand Teton National Park, Wyoming, Alpha Photo Associates. Back cover, Robert Cushman Hayes.

# The Dawn of Another New Year
## ... A Time to Renew Friendships

# IDEALS ... *We've been building friendships for over 30 years!*

*The dawn of another year ... time to reflect on the year past and the year to come.* What better time to think of friendships—old and new! There are few things more precious than friendship here at Ideals we agree. That's why, for over 30 years, IDEALS MAGAZINE has been building friendships as every year more and more people discover the unique gift-giving quality of this beautiful gift publication. What better way is there to say "hello, I'm thinking of you" to a friend or loved one than a beautiful and inspiring gift subscription to IDEALS! And, here is one gift that says "I value your friendship" not just once but six times a year!

FRIENDSHIP IDEALS is the first of 6 beautiful IDEALS issues to be published in 1979. Filled with delightful stories and poems relating the true spirit of friendships shared and the happiness received, FRIENDSHIP IDEALS is the ideal gift with which to start your personal subscription and gift subscriptions this year. There is a charming story on buttons and also the well-known children's story, "Stone Soup." There are dozens of inspiring poems and a feature on James J. Metcalfe, this issue's *Ideals Best Loved Poet*. With dazzling full color seasonal photography and artwork, this issue will brighten your winter reading pleasure and certainly do the same for those fortunate enough to receive it as a gift from you.

Why not let us build a friendship for you! Subscribe to Ideals today and send a gift subscription to each of your friends. You won't find another magazine quite so beautiful and inspiring to give ... to yourself or to your friends. Find out for yourself why we say, IDEALS, *The Magazine That Builds Friendships!* We are so sure that you and your friends will appreciate the beauty and warmth of each issue of IDEALS, that we offer you this written pledge:

*If, after receiving the first copy on your subscription, you find IDEALS MAGAZINE is not as beautiful and inspiring as you expected, just return your copy to us in its original wrapper marked "return to sender." We will cancel your subscription and the invoice due.*

Show your friends how much you care ... When you enter your subscription to IDEALS, enter a number of gift subscriptions as well. Do it TODAY! You needn't send any money now unless you prefer. Simply mark the proper area on the convenient order card or on the enclosed order blank and we'll bill you later.

## IDEALS SUBSCRIPTION PLANS

ONE YEAR ... 6 issues as published .......... $12.00
(Savings Value of $4.50 under the single copy rate.)

| | First Subscription $12.00 | Additional Subscriptions $11.00 |
|---|---|---|

TWO YEAR ... 12 issues as published ........ $19.00
(Savings Value of $14.00 under the single copy rate.)

| | First Subscription $19.00 | Additional Subscriptions $17.00 |
|---|---|---|

THREE YEAR ... 18 issues as published ....... $26.50
(Savings Value of $23.00 under the single copy rate.)

| | First Subscription $26.50 | Additional Subscriptions $24.00 |
|---|---|---|

IDEALS Single Issues ........................ $2.75

### 1979
### IDEALS' PUBLICATION SCHEDULE

| | |
|---|---|
| Friendship Ideals | Jan. |
| Easter Ideals | Mar. |
| Homespun Ideals | May |
| Carefree Days Ideals | July |
| Autumn Glory Ideals | Sept. |
| Christmas Ideals | Nov. |

# Ideals Giftbooks . . . .
## Reflections of Sentiment

the best of ideals

GOD LOVES YOU

ideals Best-Loved Poets

All giftbooks 8½" x 11"
—softcover—80 Pages
except where indicated

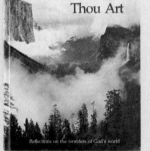

# NEW . . . BEAUTIFUL IDEALS' GIFTBOOKS

**A FRIEND IS SPECIAL** is a beautiful collection of poetry and prose to greet a special friend—either to say have a happy day or just to say thanks for being my friend. The beauty of friendship is enhanced throughout with a variety of colorful photographs which convey the true spirit of friendship as well as the nature of special friendships. **A FRIEND IS SPECIAL** is a book you will want to share with your closest friend! **04-00051—3.95**

**LOOK TO THIS DAY!** . . . and begin it in praise, trust, joy, patience, prayer and in strength. These are only a few of the titles of the sections included in this softcover volume. Each section contains poems and prose appropriate to those qualities which help each day go a little better and in thankfulness, wisdom and love. Each section is, of course, accompanied by colorful pictures featuring the beauty of nature. **04-00052—3.95**

**THE BEAUTY OF FRIENDSHIP** is a look at friendship through the poetry of June Masters Bacher. A moving and memorable tribute to friendship as God had meant it to be—a spirit of giving . . . sharing . . . caring. Colorful photographs throughout fully illustrate the beauty and warmth that friendship brings to our lives. Here is a special gift for someone special. **04-00464—1.75**

**YOUR LIGHT HAS COME** is Ideals' newest religious paperback featuring the writing of a number of well-known religious authors including Rev. Russell F. Witon. This beautiful little book affirms the belief that the future can be good for the person who loves himself and the God who has created him. Only through this love, can the full beauty and wonder of God's creation be enjoyed. The author takes the reader through this world, in all its seasons, and illustrates man's commitment to the Lord. 4¼″ x 7″—**04-00574—1.50**

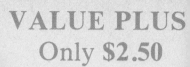